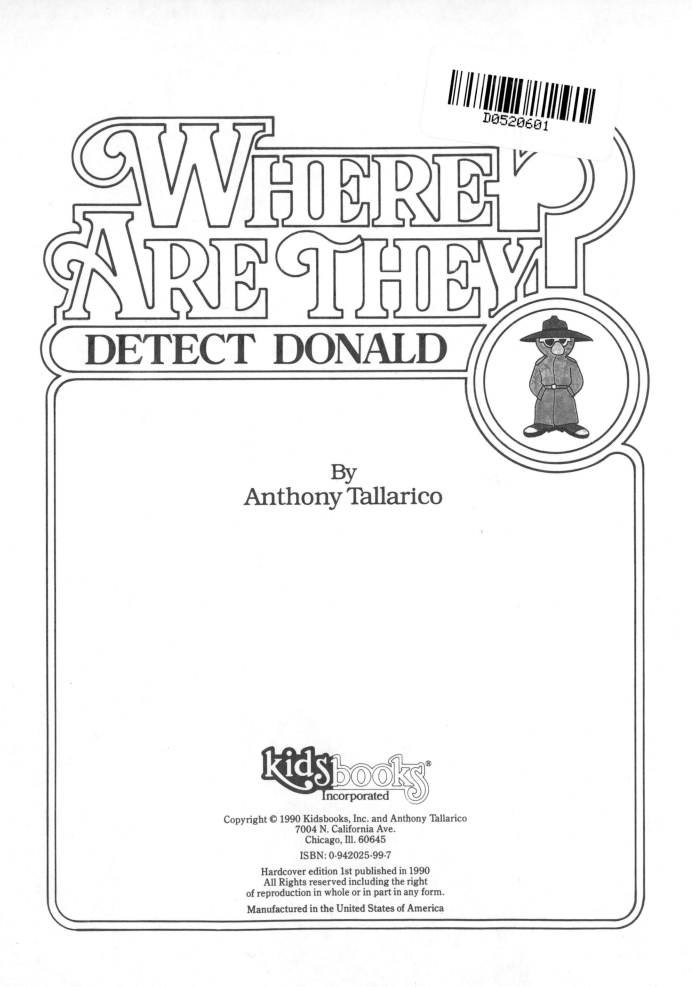

WHERE ARE THEY?

DETECT DONALD

By
Anthony Tallarico

kidsbooks®
Incorporated

Copyright © 1990 Kidsbooks, Inc. and Anthony Tallarico
7004 N. California Ave.
Chicago, Ill. 60645

ISBN: 0-942025-99-7

Hardcover edition 1st published in 1990
All Rights reserved including the right
of reproduction in whole or in part in any form.

Manufactured in the United States of America

It was a dark and rainy night in Hollywood. Detective Donald had stopped to eat at his favorite diner.

DETECT DONALD AT THE CHEEZ-E DINER AND...

- ☐ Arrow
- ☐ Bat
- ☐ Bird
- ☐ Bow ties (4)
- ☐ Bowling ball
- ☐ Cactus
- ☐ Convict
- ☐ Cook
- ☐ Crown
- ☐ Dracula
- ☐ Dragon
- ☐ Eyeglasses (3)
- ☐ Fish
- ☐ Genie
- ☐ Ghost
- ☐ Guitar
- ☐ Heart
- ☐ Humpty Dumpty
- ☐ Jack-o'-lantern
- ☐ Mouse
- ☐ Pirate
- ☐ Rabbit
- ☐ Skull
- ☐ Stars (3)
- ☐ Super heroes
- ☐ Top hat
- ☐ Two-headed man
- ☐ Waitresses (2)
- ☐ Witch
- ☐ Wristwatch

When he stepped outside, he detected something strange going on. First he saw a large group of strange characters. Then....

...Detective Donald almost got run over by a horse and carriage! There were no cars or buses and people were wearing wigs and funny hats. Detective Donald thought he saw George Washington—but it couldn't be! He decided to investigate to find out what was going on.

DETECT DONALD IN COLONIAL AMERICA AND...

- ☐ Antenna
- ☐ Baseball
- ☐ Basket
- ☐ Bell
- ☐ Ben Franklin
- ☐ Betsy Ross
- ☐ Bone
- ☐ Broom
- ☐ Bucket
- ☐ Candles (2)
- ☐ Cannonballs (4)
- ☐ Cats (2)
- ☐ Chicken
- ☐ Clock
- ☐ Dogs (2)
- ☐ Drums (3)
- ☐ Duck
- ☐ Ear of corn
- ☐ Flower vase
- ☐ Horses (4)
- ☐ Kites (2)
- ☐ Lamppost
- ☐ Mouse
- ☐ One dollar bill
- ☐ Saw
- ☐ Shopping bag
- ☐ Spinning wheel
- ☐ TV set
- ☐ Wagons (2)
- ☐ Watering can

Suddenly, two knights on horseback carrying long lances went charging by. A king, queen, knights and maidens were watching a jousting tournament. *Where was he now?* wondered Detective Donald.

DETECT DONALD IN THE MIDDLE AGES AND...

- ☐ Alligator
- ☐ Balloons (2)
- ☐ Birds (2)
- ☐ Candy cane
- ☐ Dog
- ☐ Doorbell
- ☐ Fan
- ☐ Fish
- ☐ Hot dog
- ☐ Ice-cream cone
- ☐ Jack-o'-lantern
- ☐ Jester
- ☐ King
- ☐ Kite
- ☐ Musician
- ☐ Periscope
- ☐ Pig
- ☐ Pot
- ☐ Robin Hood
- ☐ Rose
- ☐ Santa Claus
- ☐ Skull
- ☐ Sock
- ☐ Stars (2)
- ☐ Target
- ☐ Toast
- ☐ Umpire
- ☐ Unicorn
- ☐ Vendor
- ☐ Wizard

After watching the tournament for awhile, Detective Donald walked through the castle...

...and into a room filled with laughter! There were lots of cartoon characters acting silly all around him. Things were getting stranger and stranger.

DETECT DONALD IN CARTOONLAND AND...

- ☐ Balloon
- ☐ Banana peel
- ☐ Baseball
- ☐ Beehive
- ☐ Book
- ☐ Brush
- ☐ Cars (2)
- ☐ Cheese
- ☐ Clothesline
- ☐ Fire hydrant
- ☐ Fish (2)
- ☐ Fishing pole
- ☐ Flower
- ☐ Ghost
- ☐ Golf club
- ☐ Hose
- ☐ Ice-cream cone
- ☐ Magnifying glass
- ☐ Net
- ☐ Owl
- ☐ Sandwich
- ☐ Soap
- ☐ Star
- ☐ Sunglasses (2)
- ☐ Super dude
- ☐ Train engine
- ☐ Turtle
- ☐ TV set
- ☐ Umbrella

As Detective Donald walked through a hole in the wall, he heard...

..."Ahoy mates, a landlubber!" It was a pirate ship, and pirates were dashing about with swords doing battle with anyone and everyone.

DETECT DONALD AT THE PIRATES' BATTLE AND...

- ☐ Basketball
- ☐ Birds (3)
- ☐ Broom
- ☐ Candle
- ☐ Cannonballs (4)
- ☐ Captain Hook
- ☐ Cat
- ☐ Cup
- ☐ Duck
- ☐ Fish
- ☐ Football
- ☐ Guitar
- ☐ Half moon
- ☐ Headless horseman
- ☐ Hearts (2)
- ☐ Hot dog
- ☐ Jack-o'-lantern
- ☐ Knight
- ☐ Mice (7)
- ☐ Mirror
- ☐ Piano
- ☐ Rooster
- ☐ Sailboat
- ☐ Snake
- ☐ Top hat
- ☐ Treasure chest
- ☐ Turtles (3)
- ☐ Watering can
- ☐ Wooden legs (3)
- ☐ Yellow brick road

Detective Donald thought it best to quickly move on.

What was happening? Detective Donald's surroundings began to change before his very eyes! Strange buildings and bizarre creatures replaced the pirates.

DETECT DONALD IN THE WORLD OF THE FUTURE AND...

- ☐ Baby carriage
- ☐ Bat
- ☐ Bottle
- ☐ Bow
- ☐ Clothespin
- ☐ Dog
- ☐ Flat tire
- ☐ Hammer
- ☐ Key
- ☐ Kite
- ☐ Ladder
- ☐ Little red riding creature
- ☐ Mailbox
- ☐ Parachute
- ☐ Pencil
- ☐ Phonograph record
- ☐ Pocket watch
- ☐ Red wagon
- ☐ Submarine sandwich
- ☐ Schoolbag
- ☐ Sled
- ☐ Snowman
- ☐ Straw
- ☐ Teeth
- ☐ Tree
- ☐ Two-headed creature
- ☐ Tepee
- ☐ Vacuum cleaner
- ☐ Witch

Out an exit he went, and into...

...French history a few hundred years ago. He was more confused than ever. Maybe I'm just having a weird dream, he thought.

DETECT DONALD IN NAPOLEON'S FRANCE AND...

- ☐ Alligator
- ☐ Axe
- ☐ Ballerina
- ☐ Balloon
- ☐ Baker
- ☐ Bell
- ☐ Cake
- ☐ Cannon
- ☐ Dracula
- ☐ Dragon
- ☐ Duck
- ☐ Eight ball
- ☐ Firecracker
- ☐ Flower
- ☐ French poodle
- ☐ King Kong
- ☐ Medals (2)
- ☐ Mermaid
- ☐ Movie camera
- ☐ Mummy
- ☐ Old tire
- ☐ One-eyed alien
- ☐ Pinocchio
- ☐ Radio
- ☐ Rapunzel
- ☐ Sailor
- ☐ Scarecrow
- ☐ Shark
- ☐ Tarzan
- ☐ Unicorn

Detective Donald kept searching and searching for clues. Next he found himself...

...in an army camp during basic training. Some soldiers were having fun, but most were happy when training was over. Detective Donald noticed a movie camera. Hmmm, he wondered, haven't I seen one somewhere before?

DETECT DONALD AT FORT KNOCKS AND...

- [ ] Ape
- [ ] Bat
- [ ] Bird
- [ ] Bodiless ghost
- [ ] Bombs (2)
- [ ] Cactus
- [ ] Chimneys (2)
- [ ] Cook
- [ ] Dunce cap
- [ ] Fan
- [ ] Fish (2)
- [ ] Jack-o'-lantern
- [ ] Lemonade stand
- [ ] Kite
- [ ] Medal
- [ ] Oil can
- [ ] Periscope
- [ ] Pitcher
- [ ] Pot
- [ ] Rat
- [ ] Robin Hood
- [ ] Sergeant's stripes (5)
- [ ] Skulls (2)
- [ ] Slingshot
- [ ] Snake
- [ ] Sock
- [ ] Traffic ticket
- [ ] Turtle
- [ ] Volcano

Donald walked past the chow line and into...

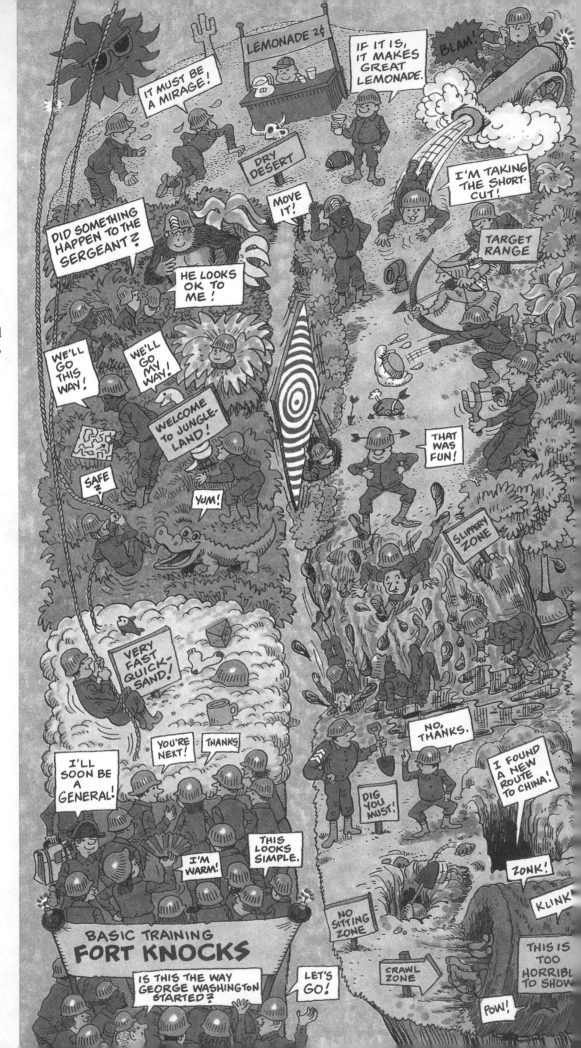

...the Roman Coliseum. But it wasn't a ruin! It was full of ancient Romans rooting for or against gladiators.

DETECT DONALD IN ANCIENT ROME AND...

- ☐ Abraham Lincoln
- ☐ Banana peel
- ☐ Bones (2)
- ☐ Boots
- ☐ Cheerleader
- ☐ Cleopatra
- ☐ Dog
- ☐ Dragons (2)
- ☐ Electric fan
- ☐ Elephant
- ☐ Football
- ☐ Giraffe
- ☐ Guitar
- ☐ Hot dog
- ☐ Hourglass
- ☐ Jester
- ☐ Kite
- ☐ Lions (3)
- ☐ Lunch boxes (2)
- ☐ Necktie
- ☐ Net
- ☐ Pig
- ☐ Raindrops (2)
- ☐ Red scarf
- ☐ Secret door
- ☐ Soccer ball
- ☐ Spears (2)
- ☐ Tin man
- ☐ Vendors (2)
- ☐ Watch
- ☐ Watering can

Detective Donald ducked out behind the big wooden horse and immediately ran into...

...a wooly mammoth! It was huge and hairy, but how did it get here? Or, how did *he* get *there?* The spear-carrying cave people frightened Detective Donald so he leapt out of their way.

DETECT DONALD IN PREHISTORIC TIMES AND...

- ☐ Ape
- ☐ Arrow
- ☐ Baby bird
- ☐ Basketball
- ☐ Bicycle
- ☐ Bone
- ☐ Book
- ☐ Burglar
- ☐ Cannon
- ☐ Chef
- ☐ Clipboard
- ☐ Helmet
- ☐ Juggler
- ☐ Kettle
- ☐ Mailbox
- ☐ Nets (2)
- ☐ Periscope
- ☐ Pole-vaulter
- ☐ Rabbit
- ☐ Rocket
- ☐ Rocking chair
- ☐ Rocking horse
- ☐ Roller skates
- ☐ Skateboard
- ☐ Skier
- ☐ Tennis racket
- ☐ Toothbrush
- ☐ Tuba
- ☐ Turtle
- ☐ Umbrella
- ☐ Witch

Donald continued on until he came to the back of a curtain. He opened it in time to hear...

...“And now...” He was standing on a stage receiving an award! But why? Then a very embarrassed Detective Donald realized that, without knowing it, he had just walked through ten movie sets!

DETECT DONALD AT THE ACADEMY AWARDS AND...

- ☐ Aliens (2)
- ☐ Arrows (2)
- ☐ Baseball cap
- ☐ Bird
- ☐ "Boo" (2)
- ☐ Bowling ball
- ☐ Broken heart
- ☐ Candle
- ☐ Cook
- ☐ Darts (5)
- ☐ Dog
- ☐ Elephant
- ☐ Envelope
- ☐ Fish
- ☐ Flower
- ☐ Fork
- ☐ Ghost
- ☐ Half moon
- ☐ Heart
- ☐ Ice skates
- ☐ Lens cap
- ☐ Masks (2)
- ☐ Microphone
- ☐ Mushroom
- ☐ Pencil
- ☐ Rabbit
- ☐ Scarf
- ☐ Skulls (2)
- ☐ Snake
- ☐ Tomahawk

LOOK FOR LAURA DETECT DONALD FIND FRANKIE SEARCH FOR SUSIE